DRABBLE II

DOUBLE CENTURY

This book is dedicated to all
those authors who, when we were
teetering on the edge, pushed us
into publishing this second
selection of Drabbles

and

to the
Royal National Institute
for the Blind

DRABBLE II
DOUBLE CENTURY

Compiled by
Rob Meades and David B. Wake

BECCON Publications

FIRST EDITION
ISBN 1-870824-15-6

1000 hardbound copies
of which the contributors
receive one copy each.

Copy no.

805

Book designed by R & A Robinson for
BECCON PUBLICATIONS
75 ROSSLYN AVENUE
HAROLD WOOD
ESSEX RM3 0RG

Photoset, Printed and Bound in Great Britain
by WBC Bristol & Maesteg

CONTENTS

ROB MEADES

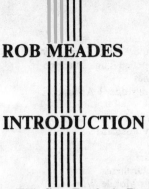

INTRODUCTION

The first Drabble Project book was published at Easter 1988. David and I were petrified. What was originally to be a twenty page photocopied booklet had become a collection of one hundred stories in hardback: we had no idea how it would be received.

We needn't have worried. Last November we gave £1000 to the R.N.I.B. "Talking Book" fund, with more money to come. And, just as importantly, our authors enjoyed themselves immensely.

This second Drabble Project book, containing one hundred stories by one hundred authors, has come about by popular demand. We've had fun. I hope you will too.

January 1990

The Drabble Project
160 Beaumont Road
Bournville
BIRMINGHAM B30 1NY

DAVID B. WAKE

DRABBLE RULES:
THE ONE HUNDRED WORD VARIANT

Introduction

Drabble is played sitting around a fire, while sipping brandy and partaking of pleasant conversation with friends. The first person to finish a novel wins.

A Doubtful History

The first game of Drabble, a name coined in a *Monty Python* sketch, was played at the beginning of the last century. The winner was Mary Shelley with *Frankenstein* and Polidori, who didn't actually finish during that stormy weekend, came second with *The Vampyre*.

The Rules

'One hundred words' must be EXACTLY one hundred words: not a syllable more, not a letter less. In addition, up to fifteen words (title, sub-titles and the like) are allowed. Hyphenated-words-are-argued-about.

The End

THE
STORIES

STEPHEN R. EALEY

NASCENT

One

I am the universe and the universe is me. I exist. I am alone. An infinite cavern of blackness surrounds me. It is warm and good.

Two

Presently, I reach out and touch a living wall surrounding my Universe. I perceive a throbbing form . . . outside. But what can be outside? Nothing else exists, does it?

Three

My universe grows smaller. Claustrophobic fears overwhelm me. Will I end? The noise still filters through, tormenting me.

Four

Somehow, I must escape. I throw myself at the living wall. Something gives. Push, press, kick. I am getting out. Kick, a blinding light is ahead ... kick ... kick ...

GAYNOR COULES

EVOLUTION

Awake.   Cold.   Light.   Warmth.   Movement.
Encounter. Food?   Eat.   Strength.   Movement.   Growth.
Encounter. Food?   Mate.   Fusion.   Fission.   Dispersion.
Encounters. Food?   Eat.   Strength.   Movement.   Growth.
Expansion.
Encounter.
Encounter.
Encounter.
            Food?
                           Mate?
                                       Movement?
Hunger.   Overcrowding. Stagnation.   Regression. Senescence.
Aggression. Destruction.   Cannibalism. Autolysm.

Dark.   Cold.   Sleep.

Awake.   Cold.   Light.   Warmth.   Movement.
Encounter. Food?   Eat.   Strength.   Movement.   Growth.
Encounter. Food?   Mate.   Fusion.   Fission.   Dispersion.
Encounter. Food?   Eat.   Strength.   Movement.   Growth.
Expansion.
Encounter.
Encounter.
Encounter.
            Food?
                           Mate?
                                       Movement?
Memory.   Stability.   Learning.   Understanding.

Dark.   Cold.   Sleep.

Awake.   Cold.   Light.   Warmth.   Movement.
Encounter. Food?   Eat.   Strength.   Movement.   Growth.
Encounter. Food?
Memory.   Stability.   Teaching.   Awareness. Control.

Dark.   Cold.   Sleep...

JONATHAN WAITE

FROM THE FOAM, APHRODITE

Consciousness returned, and with it pain: the harshness of wet sand beneath her and the burning sun on her unprotected skin.

She opened her eyes, and immediately shut them against the blinding glare. After a while she grew able to see: the beach, the receding waves, the shade of trees, impossibly distant. The tide had cast her a good distance up the shore, but there was a considerable stretch of baking sand to be crossed before she could rest.

After which, she realised, the next problem would be persuading one of the males to follow her out of the water.

MIKE CONEY

AN ENTRY IN THE GALACTIC WILDLIFE ENCYCLOPEDIA, COPYRIGHT 2046

BALEEN RAT

This tiny creature was the last mammalian species to be discovered on the planet Earth, when in 1996 a group was found near Tuktoyaktuk, North-west Territory.

PARADOXICAL FAMILY TREE

Descended from the huge Mesonychid of the Palaeocene, the insignificant baleen rat is the direct ancestor of the giant blue whale and other *balaenidae*.

CREATURE OF LEGEND

Feeding baleen rats probably originated the "Phantom Mothersuckers" of Inuit legend. Noisily inhaling the mosquito infested air, they snare insects against the baleen curtain in their mouths.

PROMISING FUTURE

Since the insecticide ban of 2003, the baleen rat has spread rapidly world-wide.

C. J. CHERRYH

A MUCH BRIEFER HISTORY OF TIME

Long ago a microbe decided to be god. It fissioned and became polytheistic. Rapidly the pond filled with gods fissioning and dividing until a passing rainstorm carried a number of the divinities downstream. They fissioned and filled a lake, which fed a river, which fed the sea. Within a billion years only isolate bodies of water lacked divinity. The microbes teleologically evolved bipedal colonies as transportation – which had drawbacks: these mobile colonies proved self directed and schismatic. The free swimming microbes (equally teleologically) maximized their reproductive potential by infiltrating mobile colonies which, responding to selective pressure, developed a space program.

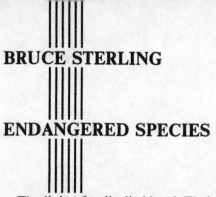

BRUCE STERLING

ENDANGERED SPECIES

The living fossils died hard. Their final outpost ruptured, spilling gaudy sprays of air and moisture into the chilly vacuum. Their successors (and killers) spread their hollow skins miles wide in the wholesome X-Ray glare of the sun.

Brilliantly advanced space-born Posthumans had annihilated the obnoxious, retrograde presence of 'Man in Space.' The wretchedly out-dated humans, with their bloated O'Neill Colonies, their ridiculously unfit bilateral symmetry, their water-sopping, oxygen-huffing innards, were at last consigned to the ash heap of stellar history.

"Now comrades! At last! On to the glorious stars!"

"Not yet."

Toward Earth they turned their cool, unsympathetic gaze . . .

ROGER ZELAZNY

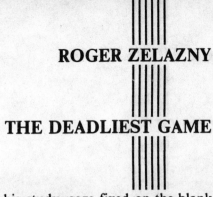

THE DEADLIEST GAME

Uncle Dudley sat in his study, gaze fixed on the blank screen of the set which hung on the wall before him. A rack of rifles hung to his right, flanked by the heads of Cape Buffalo and lion.

"Which was the deadliest of all?" I asked him.

He nodded directly ahead.

I studied the machine closely, saw the silvery ears laid flat along its brow as if it had been attacking when it took the hit. 30.06, I judged.

"Extinct now, aren't they?" I asked.

He fingered the scar on his cheek and nodded.

"Good thing, too," he said.

LIZ HONEYWILL

COLOURS

I watch as the vermilion cat stretches on the plum coloured grass, basking in the light of the emerald sun. He gazes raptly as a flock of aquamarine sparrows fly overhead, and his ears prick as one descends to land in a nearby magenta tree.

This is the way I see since the surgeons hacked my brain. Imprisoned by colour, I can only stare as the glare of the world cascades upon and around me.

I watch as the vermilion cat rises, gracefully stalking a ruby mouse. He pounces and all around me I see the splashes of saffron blood.

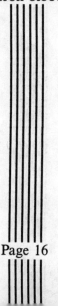

MARION EDWARDS

TAPESTRY

Here misery ended. My existence was a threat to another woman so my life was forfeit. Three Crowns said to be mine, but my religion brought far greater happiness.

I stitched my sorrows and joys into needlework. White for the lilies of France, purple for the heather of Scotland, green for the English countryside. Warm, comfortable crimson for the friendship and care of my four Maries. Black for the hearts of men who murdered and hated, grey for my captivity, my hopelessness, the castles in which I was confined, lastly red for my blood which was shed here in Fotheringay.

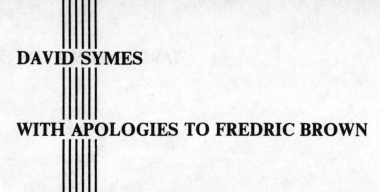

DAVID SYMES

WITH APOLOGIES TO FREDRIC BROWN

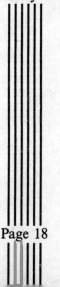

God the all seeing and all wise began brewing his newest batch of ambrosia. His finest yet.

He prepared the ingredients with immaculate care; only the best fruits, the purest sugar, went into the vessel, then the trillion decalitres of rain water.

When all was prepared he added the yeast and went off to bed.

Unfortunately God the all seeing and all wise had forgotten to turn the heating down. As the mixture warmed, its giant fermentation rose and began to drown the universe.

The first the earthmen knew of this was when The Sun Sank Slowly In The Yeast.

PETER NEGUS

CONSOLIDATED HOLDINGS
IN CHURCH TAKEOVER?

City speculation led to intense dealings in British Church shares following Consolidated Holdings chairperson Flora Parkinson's statement that she would "Not rule out a spiritual investment." Cons-Hold, as owner of 35% of London Metropolitan sub-1000m Upwards Building Areas (UBAs), has been seeking to add value to its empty space by consecration.

British Church has suffered cash-flow problems since its attempt to diversify into the fast food business. Start-up costs on its ChristBurgers chain were very high, despite good initial profits from its flagship St. Paul's outlet.

British Church was up 43 to 159. Consolidated Holdings was down $1\frac{1}{2}$ to 95.

RACHEL POLLACK

GENERAL ALL PURPOSE FAIRY TALE

Gluck builds condominiums for the Brazilian ants; two months later, they will help him when the Yellow Emperor orders him to recircuit the communications satellite. The evil sisters hide in the womb, gnawing away at Snow White's uterus. In his skyscraper apartment Boots sorts through the remnants of his brothers. Outside, the ambassador from the Land of Pigs sits looking at a brain-scan of Jakob Grimm. This is the way the world ends, Boots thinks. He touches glossy photographs, himself laughing with the King of Birds, Gluck fingering the dice of immortality. It furthers one to drink the Great Water.

STEVE JONES

ECOLOGY OF THE DWARF ELF

In fantasy games all dwarves are bearded males, with the obviously absurd excuse that the females stay at home (or have beards like the males. Ha! Ha!).

Similarly, all elves have 'males' with no facial hair who are notoriously effeminate, and 'females' with boyish figures, making them completely indistinguishable. A pathetically transparent attempt to conceal the terrible truth.

The conclusion is inescapable. Dwarves and elves are the males and females of the same species! This explains the nature of the curious 'ancient animosity' between them, and why there are so few of them now.

Next month: Ecology of the Munchkin.

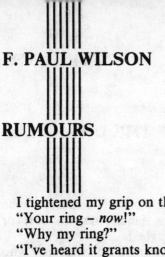

F. PAUL WILSON

RUMOURS

I tightened my grip on the dwarf's throat.

"Your ring – *now*!"

"Why my ring?"

"I've heard it grants knowledge! Power!"

"It won't fit!"

"I've heard it fits all!" I squeezed his throat. "Give it!"

"Stop!" he rasped and stuck out his hand. "Take it!"

I pulled it from his finger and dropped him, then pushed the ring against my fingertip. It expanded, slipping easily over the knuckle.

"Ah! Now –"

The dwarf suddenly looked larger, while I... I was *shrinking*! And the ring – it wouldn't come off!

"But – ?"

The looming former dwarf leered. "Now you know: Don't believe everything you hear."

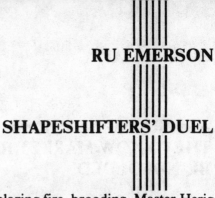

RU EMERSON

SHAPESHIFTERS' DUEL

Erfang sat before a blazing fire, brooding. Master Herig gone – dead, likely – his fellow apprentice Stolph his only rival now. But where?

He started; a skunk came to the fire, Shifted, becoming man. "Acknowledge me master."

"Never!" Erfang Shifted, becoming bird, dove at human eyes. Missed as Stolph Shifted, becoming puma, hooking Erfang's wing. Feathers fell; Erfang Shifted, becoming bear. He swatted.

"Herig is gone, I am master!" Stolph shouted, becoming again skunk.

"I am better!" Erfang choked, becoming porcupine.

Stolph screamed, and skunk-to-badger tore quills free. The fire Shifted, rose, swallowed both. "Arrogant damned apprentices," Herig growled, becoming man.

SUNA AKIAH

A WARNING TO THOSE WHO THINK THEY KNOW MARKET RESEARCH BLINDFOLDED

An old woman tottering home met a hungry ogre which snarled, waving hairy arms. She ordered him aside.

"Don't my claws scare you?" he asked.

"No!" she yelled, brushing by.

Next day it happened again.

"Don't my sharp teeth terrify you?" enquired the ogre.

"No!" she cried, pushing him aside and continuing.

The exasperated ogre tried again, unsuccessfully. "But doesn't my appearance frighten you?" he begged.

"No!" She went on her way.

The ogre, whose ogredom relied on terrifying victims to death before eating them, went away disgraced and died.

And an old blind woman survived to describe an ogre.

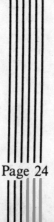

JOE HALDEMAN

UNTITLED

Once upon a time, a pretty little princess strolled down a wooded path. She happened upon a troll. She screamed.

"Fear not," said the troll. "I am an alien from another planet. I won't eat you, because your protein would sicken me."

"Ah. Then thou wouldst have thy way with me," she said, batting her barely post-pubescent eyelashes.

"No," the creature said sadly. "I reproduce by budding, and have no interest in you that way."

"Oh," she said, crestfallen. "Thou hast no interest in me at all?"

He took her hands. "But I do. I *am* a troll. Trolls lie."

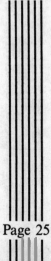

STEVE DAVIES

UNTITLED

The sorcerer had reached the final spell. Surely he would never have started upon such a dangerous undertaking save for the lure of gold, and now the fear was upon him. But all was ready and he whispered the last words of the invocation.

Within the circle, a fearsome figure appeared. It spoke, "Foolish mortal! Here is the Circle of Conjuration but where thy protective pentacle?" It slithered towards him.

"Hold!"

A cowled figure stepped from the shadows bearing a vast, red, iron-bound tome.

"You thought this just an ordinary invocation, but tonight, Lucifer Beelzebub Satan, This Is Your Life!"

Page 26

SUE BEASLEY

OUT OF THE FIRE INTO THE FRYING PAN

Sheal was forced into the shrine by those who chased her. Enclosed by sanctuary, she sighed with relief and muttered a prayer of thanks to Saint Pan. The place seemed deserted except for the carved statue of the woodland saint.

The remote shrine was high on a stony hill overlooking the old forest, but it was not its location that stirred unquiet thoughts in Sheal. Somewhere a bell chimed and the shrine's holy keeper appeared, napkin tucked under his chin. Only then did she recall the tales she had heard ...

"Ah," said the keeper, licking his lips. "Dinner is served."

MARY GENTLE

AMBITIONS

The decadent ruler of a dying civilisation faced the enemy armies, with his sentient sword:

"Blood-drinker is never drawn but it creates carnage before it can again be sheathed!"

Just a minute...

There was hesitation in the sword's spirit-voice.

"What do you mean, *just a minute*? There are thousands of psychopaths out there!"

Can we talk about this?

"Talk?! You're a guaranteed sentient sword, with an unappeasable appetite for the souls and blood of men; what's the problem?"

You see, I only ever wanted...

Screaming warriors thundered across the battlefield, reducing the ruler to bloody gobbets.

... to be a ploughshare.

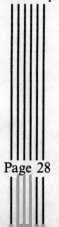

KATE SOLEY

THE WYVERN'S HOARD

A wyvern sat in his cave, guarding his hoard. It fitted neatly under his right foot. One jewel he had; in the sunlight it shone with many colours. In the cave, it lay dully under his claw.

He himself was far more beautiful, both in and out of the light, glowing with many-coloured scales that shone of themselves.

The wyvern waited for thieves to come for his hoard, for he knew that was how hoards grew. Thieves wore fine armour, carried jewelled swords, and died quickly.

It never occurred to him that they might prefer his hide to his hoard...

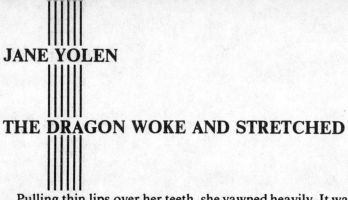

JANE YOLEN

THE DRAGON WOKE AND STRETCHED

Pulling thin lips over her teeth, she yawned heavily. It was winter and she was white again, the blood running thin through her leathery wings.

Behind her towered the black mountains; it had been a snowless year.

She shook herself, dislodging several branches from her nest, then leaped into the sky.

When they shot her the blood blossomed bright against her white breast. Falling to the ground, she shook the mountain, too large for them to cart away.

By morning, when they returned with knives, she was covered with nestlings lapping at her blood like human babes at the breast.

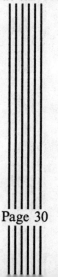

ANNE HARCOURT

WATERSHED

"Look! There she is," a voice shouted from the jetty. The seaweed smacked her face. She laughed.

Her two companions were now swimming straight towards her. She dived like a dolphin, enjoying the water. They came nearer, she bobbed up behind them. Confused, they circled, treading water.

Tiring of the game she swam to the shore. The silent crowd on the beach ignored her, unblinking round eyes fixed out to sea. She walked straight through them, they were frozen.

Reaching the dunes she stopped. Pulling the seaweed from her hair Susan looked down. She left no footprints in the sand.

STEVE RASNIC TEM

THE ADOPTIONS

She awakes with dark in the room. The dark cries all night, all day. She takes it to her breast.

She awakes with shadow in the room. The shadow is lost, wandering from chair to cabinet, to door. She takes it to bed, never to sleep the night again.

She wakes with creatures in her room, crying and mewling, eyes luminous in the night. She surrounds them with her arms, rocking them to sleep.

Now the townspeople never see her. At night the moon is red, the clouds slip to the ground. The woods curl around the houses and growl.

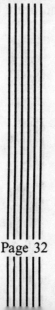

NEIL GAIMAN

NICHOLAS WAS...

Older than sin, and his beard could grow no whiter. He wanted to die.

The dwarfish natives of the arctic caverns did not speak his language, but conversed in their own, twittering tongue, conducted incomprehensible rituals, when they were not actually working in the factories.

Once every year they forced him, sobbing and protesting, into Endless Night. During the journey he would stand near every child in the world, leave one of the dwarves' invisible gifts by its bedside. The children slept, frozen into time.

He envied Prometheus and Loki, Sisyphus and Judas. His punishment was harsher.

Ho.

Ho.

Ho.

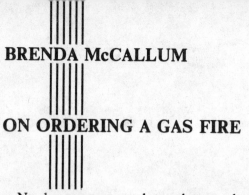

BRENDA McCALLUM

ON ORDERING A GAS FIRE

No longer any need to observe the ritual. Cleaning, carrying, tending the flames, all that was for the past. New ways beckoned – buttons to push, dials to turn, these would set her free. She stood at the crossroads unsure of her path.

"Put out your hand to the new technology, that is better than drudgery and easier than known ways."

Her fingers trembled, but gathering her courage she stepped into the future and sighed. More freedom – leisure to enjoy herself and lead life to the full. She even bought a barbecue, picked up some charcoal and went home to celebrate!

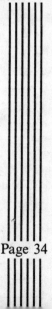

JANE STABLEFORD

SEX LIVES OF HOUSEWIVES

I have been asked to write the foreword for a book entitled *Sex Lives of Housewives*. I was rather annoyed that the editor would allow only one hundred words for my purpose.

"Not too much foreplay," he explained wittily.

"How like a man," I fumed.

"But he is right!" exclaimed my collaborator. "The book is intended to be *descriptive*, not *prescriptive*."

I accept this point of view and feel that the recording of it makes an admirable introduction to the topic in question.

May this book prove sufficiently interesting to carry our readers ... male or female ... through to the climax.

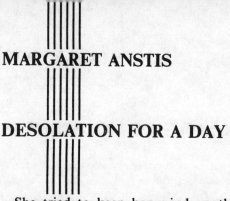

MARGARET ANSTIS

DESOLATION FOR A DAY

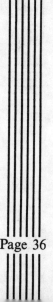

She tried to keep her mind on the jobs in hand, but without him at her side she knew her life would never seem the same again.

When he left this morning he had taken a part of her with him. She moved from room to room trying to curb her desolation. Reminders of him were everywhere. She supposed by now he had completely forgotten about her. She remembered clearly how he had left her without a backward glance.

Momentarily she hated him for making her so unhappy, but all he had done was become five and gone to school.

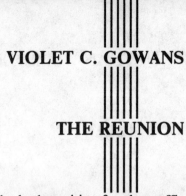

VIOLET C. GOWANS

THE REUNION

She stood hesitating on the kerb, waiting for the traffic lights to change. Then, suddenly, she heard a shout.

Turning to her left, something she saw rooted her to the spot. Striding towards her was the only man she had ever loved, looking as handsome as he did some 40 years ago when they last met.

Fascinated, she watched his approach, flattered that he had recognised her. Now, at last he was taking her arm; it was just like old times.

Looking into her eyes, he said, in those memorably seductive tones, "Madam, may I help you across the road?"

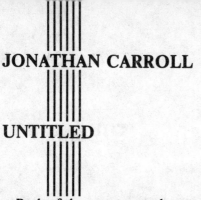

JONATHAN CARROLL

UNTITLED

Both of them were utterly astonished and thrilled to find themselves in bed the night they met. Something neither had ever done (or *imagined* doing) before.

She was tall and light, he dark and short. He came up to her chin when they stood by the side of the bed, embracing. "If you ate me, I'd only fill you to your throat. An hors d'oeuvres!"

It was meant as a joke. But looking at him, she realized how short he *was*. And what had been lovely, filled with infinite possibilities, was suddenly as dull and precise as a tape measure.

TONY CHESTER

JUST THE WAY YOU ARE

Back in the tank, having nearly exhausted his two minutes outside, the hammer fell from his median tentacle. In his leftside upper was a photograph. She had come to investigate the noise. She knelt, sobbing, over the ruins of her recent purchases.

"I hate you!" she cried, scattering the mangled remnants of the Skeletal Displacer. She stood, her feet further crushing the debris of the Muscular Enhancer. She threw the Tracheal Filter; it bounced off the glass that separated them.

Looking through his milky atmosphere at her tears he said, "I love you," pressing their wedding photo to the glass.

CHRIS BUNT

CORDON BLUES

Newly wed, they survived on salads while she learned to cook. She went to classes, practised, improved.

Later she experimented, eagerly extended her range. He was a happy guinea-pig. Not everything was successful. Her first lasagne sauce was delicious but the pasta tasted like stale elastic. Home-made bread was thrown out, and ignored by the birds.

She persevered, became more expert, started demonstrating her skills. She made gorgeous gateaux, melt-in-the-mouth meringues. He became more rotund.

Now she demonstrates her art on television and travels the world seeking new recipes, while he survives on salads and gloomily learns how to cook.

JOAN AIKEN

DEVIL'S FOOD

The Ransomes move to the wilderness to preserve their child from disease and wickedness. Charles studies the Albigensian heresy, Ruth is learning to levitate.

Reading *Pinocchio* to six year old Cathy, Charles realises that it is a Cathar tract; Pinocchio is the terrestrial body, Satan's emissaries are the Cat and Fox, the Azure fairy is an angel, Pinocchio's imprisonment in the whale is the *consolamentium*.

Bored by this, Cathy goes to the kitchen for food but Ruth, having achieved levitation, can't descend to open the fridge.

Cathy wanders out to the hen run for eggs, which are all salmonella infected.

JOHN STEWART

BEST BEFORE

The young couple stripped and moved across the hotel room to a shallow depression which appeared to be the bed. Despite its unusual design it was comfortable, tissue paper material padding them from the foam plastic base and warm air enveloping them as they lay. Anticipation of each other, they presumed, found them gasping as they flopped together.

Rubbing the scales of his face, forked tongue testing for odours, he examined the selection. One pair, apart from slight blueness caused by the gas packing, appeared very fresh beneath the cling film wrapper. The label read:

Whole Humans
Best before: IVVVXI.

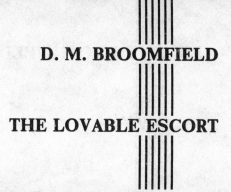

D. M. BROOMFIELD

THE LOVABLE ESCORT

They took my love away. Two burly men with tackle and rope. They tied you up and suspended you in the air. Gently my poor heart cried, but they heard me not. They do not know our suffering, leaky roof and punctured tubes. We fought the rust together and now you lie, your wheels askew, wipers gone and windows broken.

What times we had, trips to the coast and AA lifts home. My trusty steed you served me well. My pride and joy. Your number I will remember always, my escort, coloured blue. Your worth, only a five pound note.

ELIZABETH ROTHWELL

THE TRYST

She stood beneath the clock at Victoria Station while the crowd on the concourse milled around her.

She had just decided to wait for five more minutes when he came up to her, just as she had imagined him – young, presentable and rather embarrassed.

"Brenda?" he asked and, when she nodded, shook her hand and said, "Let's go and have a cup of tea and really get to know each other."

With her arm in his, they walked towards the refreshment room. After two unsuccessful waits, the third time had been lucky. But what a pity her name was Audrey.

SARAH LEFANU

THE MOTHER'S DREAM

Chapter One

In the dream the fetch (apparition, double, or wraith of a living person) oozed through her closed bedroom window. Materialising monstrously in front of her, it winked, and set off in search of her children.

Chapter Two

Is it not enough, she though despairingly, that I brood over how to save my girls from the wolf in the forest, my boys from the roaring one-eyed giant, and both from the conflagration that may annihilate us all? Yet now I must save them from myself.

Chapter Three

In the dream she ran, panicking, to her children. They all ignored her. That, at least, was realistic.

CAROL SHETLER

A GENIE'S FONDEST WISH

Ibt-al-Jauzah, otherwise known as the genie in Aladdin's lamp, studied the faded papyrus once more.

"A djinn who has no human master for one thousand years will never again have to grant a mortal's wish."

Since Aladdin's demise, Ibt-al-Jauzah had evaded all humans. "Only a year to go – then I'll be out of this damned lamp!" he gloated.

He'd found the perfect hiding spot – as space junk. Few humans cared what was up there.

Until a metal-detector satellite, on a search for rare alloys, brushed its sweep-arm against the lamp.

Ibt-al-Jauzah cried to his new master:

"But you're not human...!"

HELEN McNABB

IF WISHES WERE HORSES

The heatwave showed no sign of breaking. The sun blazed in the unbroken blue sky, only the short summer nights brought respite. The small girl sat on the withered grass under an unhappy tree looking wistfully at the shop. Inside were cold drinks and ice lollies. She wished fervently that she had some money to buy something, anything not hot.

The shabby dream pedlar watched her. In his gift was the magic of imagination; to give, however briefly, whatever she wanted.

"Hey, kid, would you like a nice dream?"

"Oh YES! Please! I'd like a chocolate one in a cornet!"

ELSIE W. K. DONALD

POOR SOUL

On an empty chair in a corner of the room sits a lonely little boy. Nobody speaks to him, everyone ignores him. He thinks this is his penance.

Once he ran and shouted, but his elders said, "Little boys should be seen and not heard," and when he became ill they said, "It's a punishment," and when he got worse, "It's a judgement."

Finally they cried over him and pretended he had gone away, so he came and sat in the chair, waiting for them to notice him. Nobody has, and nobody will, for the chair is empty. Poor soul.

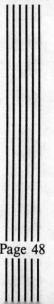

THELMA BRADFORD

THE FAMILY

One year ago today their daughter had been chosen. She had been selected because of her beauty and innocence.

Her parents knew it was the greatest of honours, they loved her, they were proud of her, never had a year passed so quickly.

Dressed in white, gold hair shining she waited. This was the last day of her reign. The chariot was at the door. Her father kissed her, her mother held her tightly, she gently pulled away, walked proudly out. Her last triumphant ride to the altar of sacrifice, to die to ensure a great harvest for the people.

JOHN SLADEK

RADIO CATS

Henry Aldrich and Homer Brown were in the Aldrich attic when they opened an old trunk and found a gigantic penis. It had belonged to Henry's grandfather, who used it in the Spanish/American War.

"Holy Cow, Hen. Looks almost alive."

"Sure. A thing like this never really dies. You just put it in water and it's as good as new."

"Oh boy! Could I borrow it for my date with Agnes?"

"Gee, I don't know, Homer. You mean as a kind of conversation piece?"

"Sure, you know. For making small talk."

And that's how AIDS got started in Centerville.

JENNIFER GEE

TEN

A man in a green coat took him out of the dark place. There was bright light and a medicine smell. He hurt. He tried to mew and twitched his tail. The woman who called herself mummy stroked him. "Goodbye, Timmy."

When he awoke a woman in a white coat took him out of the dark place. There was bright light and a medicine smell. He was wet. He cried and clenched his fists. A woman who called herself mummy took him in her arms. "Hello, baby."

He'd have to be more careful this time. Humans only had one life.

BETTY DIBB

AT THE THIRD STROKE

The time will be 6.25 precisely.

Visitors stroll uncertainly or stride purposefully, flowers held aloft. Everyone embraces. Kisses are exchanged, hands held, eyes shine.

Parents grin, grandparents coo and great grandparents are allowed a peek before settling into chairs provided for the elderly.

Names are suggested and rejected. Both families nervously hope to persuade the other of names more suitable than those already carefully selected and chosen during the long pregnancy.

Everybody takes a look.

Congratulations

To Caroline and Christopher – a son, born 6.25.

Sister speaks quietly to weeping woman.

Commiserations

To Mary – husband died 6.25.
(Suffered two previous strokes.)

Page 52

STEVEN J. BLYTH

THE NIGHT HAS A THOUSAND EYES

I was sitting at my desk behind the post office counter when he charged in brandishing his shotgun and demanding cash. Then there was a sound like thunder. It didn't hurt. All I felt was a thud throughout my body.

For years before that day I'd wondered if there was anything beyond death. After that day I knew. As my corpse hit the floor I continued to stare at the armed robber's fiendish face.

And I've stared in that direction ever since, watching people going about their lives. I consider myself fortunate to have died in such an interesting place.

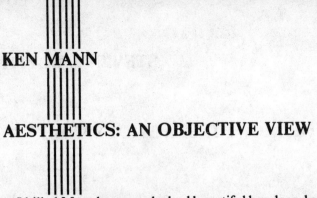

KEN MANN

AESTHETICS: AN OBJECTIVE VIEW

I killed Mary because she had beautiful hands and as soon as I saw them I knew I had to have them. With Anne it was her nose that attracted me. I told Eleanor that her blood was worth bottling and I meant it.

You see I have an ideal of womanhood, but I have yet to meet a woman who embodies it more than in part. I have approached this problem in a spirit of compromise.

I have in this room the most beautiful woman in the world, provided of course that you count the contents of every jar.

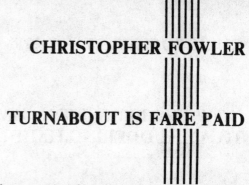

CHRISTOPHER FOWLER

TURNABOUT IS FARE PAID

The things in the tunnels of the London Underground sometimes appear at night. They hide beneath spiral stairwells, listening out for shoes on steel.

Hi-Top watched the last train pass before scrawling his band across the tiles. Drawn by the warmth of his tattooed skin, they studied each meticulous design. The Hip-Hop hid their scrabblings as they dragged him into inky darkness. Longlife batteries kept the music high as they stripped the hearts and daggers from him.

Next morning, commuters fainted as his skin congealed on tunnel walls. Fame for Hi-Top! Musically, he'd wanted to be all over London's underground.

CHRISTOPHER STASHEFF

HOW THE REBELLION CAME
TO A SHUDDERING HALT

In 2509, Luna's rebel colonists declared their independence of Terra, and backed up their declaration with the threat of launching huge boulders toward the Earth. Unfortunately for them, the Terran Government's top scientists had just perfected a technique for manufacturing quantum black holes. They built one in orbit, fired it from a gravitic linear accelerator, and skipped it past the rebels' headquarters in Clavius. The intensity of its gravitational field triggered crustal quakes all over Luna. The rebels surrendered immediately, knowing the Terran Government could wreck their colony – because, as their leader pointed out, "The miss is a harsh moonstress."

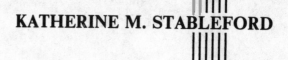

KATHERINE M. STABLEFORD

PARADISO

They found Fred Pilgrim blind drunk sitting on top of the Pearly Gates, gnawing on a roasted angel-wing and smoking a home-made cigar. They had already found the tree of knowledge bare of fruit; Fred had built a still and made the apples into cider.

He was hauled up before God, who demanded an explanation.

"Well," he said, "I've been in Heaven now for two million years, and I am utterly, completely and mind-bogglingly BORED. I was just trying to PEP things up a bit."

"Well, Fred," said God, "if that's the way you feel, you'd better try life DOWNSTAIRS."

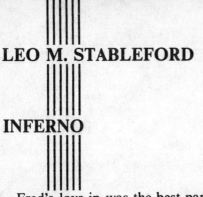

LEO M. STABLEFORD

INFERNO

Fred's love-in was the best party ever held in Hell. The lake of fire went out and the cauldrons all boiled dry. When Lucifer arrived to demand an explanation his archdemons were stoned out of their minds.

"Hey, Man," they said, "don't be uptight. It's COOL, Man, enjoy it!"

"COOL!" cried Lucifer, in anguish.

"That's the way we like it," they told him, "and we've given up hassling the damned."

"The thing is," said Fred, helpfully, "after two million years even PAIN is utterly, mind-bogglingly BORING."

"Well," said Lucifer, "if HELL is too boring for you, you'll absolutely loathe PURGATORY."

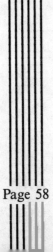

BRIAN M. STABLEFORD

PURGATORIO

Two million years had passed and not a single soul had been elevated from Purgatory.

God, suspecting diabolical influence, summoned Lucifer, who said: "It's not MY fault! It's that Fred Pilgrim. He's teaching them all techniques of transcendental meditation and helping them to raise their self-esteem. They're no more interested in self-improvement than they are in wickedness."

God sighed. "What am I to do with him?" he asked. "Wherever he goes, he's a misfit and a TROUBLE-MAKER."

"Reincarnate him," suggested Lucifer, "as something utterly and horribly INSIGNIFICANT."

Here on Earth we had better prepare for a plague of laid-back fleas.

KATHY WESTHEAD

THE PET

"Please can we, Mum? Just for one night, honest."

Lee's big eyes mirrored the animal crouching in her hands.

"It was in the playground, and Miss Shah said it couldn't stay there, and I think it's hurt its wing and Kevin's got a hutch at home somewhere and he's going to ask his mum and . . ."

Well, it stayed with us and grew stronger. But it never was a pet, always a wild thing. As its wing mended, its flights got longer. It left one dusk, the flames sparking from its mouth as its leathery wings carried it from our lives.

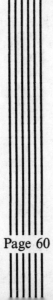

WINIFRED WAKE

ONLY FAMILY?

I geared my 60th birthday party to the enjoyment of my three young grand daughters, and their two 'toddler' cousins. I had their favourite party food and games in the sunny garden – video, cake, candles, presents, toasts, balloons. Plenty of excited laughter – a great success I joyfully thought.

Also present were Grand Father, two Aunts, one Uncle, two 'honorary' young Aunties, the Dad and Mum, and me,

When the time came for departure and thanks, my eldest grand daughter, ten, gently took my hand, and said, so sadly, "It was a lovely party Gran, what a pity no one came."

CHERRY WILDER

THE BETA SYNDROME

Captain William Noble and the rescue team watched the biosurvey hut. Had alien bioprocesses unbalanced biologist Bruno Baumgartner? Biomedic Elizabeth Bright breathed:

"He's bewitched by the beauty of Brimboria..."

"Biospores are infiltrating our masks!" insisted sergeant Robert Manly. "Breeding in our brains! Boss, we'll go bonkers!"

"Biolinguistic breakdown!" barked Noble. "With alliterative brain-washing!"

Bruno burst bellowing from the bushes.

"Breakthrough! Biostructural beta-bonding begins. Bill! Bob! Be Bruno's brothers! Betty Bright..."

She blushed. "Bruno's Bride..."

"Both brain-washed!" bemoaned Noble.

"Begone bigots!" boomed Baumgartner.

"Better beam up, Boss!"

They back-tracked, battling insidious befuddlement. Brimboria was left to the murmuring of innumerable Bs.

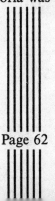

BARRINGTON J. BAYLEY

GALIMATIAS

"Come aboard my galleass!" beguiled the gallant. "We shall dine on galantine and dance a galliard!" How they gallivanted, he galligaskinned and gallooned, she girlish and gyring. A gala! Gaddings galore! But his galravaging ship graduated into the galaxy. "'Tis done by Galilean science and galvanics, gallied gal. Ill-gained gallium and galena fills our hold – and you are mine."

What gales of tears! Till gunned and grave, royal galleons englobed the pirate. He anointed her from a gallipot.

"Gallop to the fray, you galoots!"

"What a gallimaufry!"

"'Tis but a galanty show," he muttered, when they showed him the gallows.

STEVE BULL

THE WISH OF THE CONQUEROR

Having conquered the Mongol Horsemen, the great Priest-king Amtal summoned the demon K'zal to his palace with an incantation obtained from a sage at knifepoint. "I demand that you grant me a wish on my day of triumph," he shouted.

The demon leered at him. "Just the one?" he asked. "How very restrained."

"I have just conquered all the world," said Amtal, "and now I must rule it all despite the efforts of my enemies. My wish is simple. Remove the biggest obstacle to world peace!"

"With pleasure," replied the demon and Amtal disappeared in a puff of blue smoke.

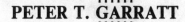

PETER T. GARRATT

MILLENNIUM ENDS: NATURAL GENEROSITY ENTAILS LAWBREAKER'S ESCAPE

For a thousand years and a day, the International Court condemned me to endure these walls.

Those fools, who could hardly believe in my survival, when they heard, or credit my arrest! They were pygmies, ignorant of the subtlety of my science, failing to understand the nature and purpose of my experiments! Weaklings, daring to sentence *me*; yet too squeamish to shoot me, as men shoot men. Now they are dust, and I, superman, survive.

For today is the anniversary: the thousand years are over, and tomorrow, when the sun rises above that dreary cell-block roof, I shall be released.

JOHN LYDECKER

GOOSECHASER

The first thing I saw when I stepped out of the time machine was the look on their faces. I'd expected more of a welcome.

"Another failed attempt," the boss-man said, which really annoyed me.

"You're right, I didn't use the rifle," I said, "but give me some credit. I broke into the Academy instead. I changed some records and switched some papers. I stuck around long enough to be sure he'd been accepted. History changes, nobody dies."

No-one said a word. They showed him a newsreel.

In grainy monochrome a tall, blonde führer now stood by the podium.

Damn.

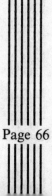

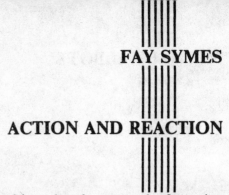

FAY SYMES

ACTION AND REACTION

The traveller returned in a thunderous crash of merging cross-polarity that shook the deepest foundations of his laboratory. His flimsy silver pyramid shimmered and wavered while inside it his figure coalesced into reality slowly, like water solidifying into ice; deepening in colour from faint pastels to brown and grey. His ecstatic expression illuminated the room as he threw off the restraints, stumbling to the shocked young woman who eyed him with alarm.

"I did it! I assassinated Vulpender when he was a baby. The greatest tyrant of all time is dead!"

"Who?" said his wife. "And anyway, who are you?"

MICHAEL ABBOTT

FORESIGHT

We had been hiking through the Greek mountains when, towards evening, we came upon an old man sitting by the side of the track. The scarring at his wrists and ankles suggested some mistreatment in the past, and the knotted flesh to the right of his stomach something far worse. Yet these were old wounds, and what made us stop in shock was the look – sane, not mad – of final despair that he turned on us. In halting Greek we asked him its cause.

"I was named foresight," came his reply, "and yet the gift I gave mankind was fire."

IAN WATSON

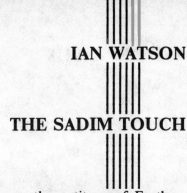

THE SADIM TOUCH

In the mythology of Thrae, the antitype of Earth, a counterpart to every terrestrial legend exists. The dowser Suehtemorp is mascot of the fire brigade. Aporue raped a cow. Susej was the son of the devil.

Consider the poignant example of King Sadim who prayed to the Gods to make everything he touched turn into ingots...

Due to the mytho-exclusion principle they could not oblige. Thereafter Sadim sat on a dunghill, ate ordure, and his once beloved Queen quite literally became a complete shit.

Beware of wishing for what has already been granted on the far side of the sun!

EVE DEVEREUX

WORD-PROCESSOR

The door slides open silently and then, after the man has entered the room, slides closed equally silently.

He sits down in front of the computer, and for a few moments stares at its glowing green eye. Then he puts his hands forwards and settles his fingers on the keyboard.

For nearly a minute his fingers are motionless, but then they start to move. Words begin to course swiftly through his brain, conjuring up new images, new ideas.

After some hours, his fingers stop moving. He stands up, moves away from the computer, and begins to speak a perfect poem.

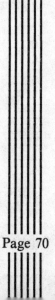

JAMES CAWTHORN

LIFE STORY

Mavedae. My last reader. Her thoughts were the last to energise and animate my image in the ancient, living book. With them, my world seemed limitless – the cities on the golden horizon, the stars beyond, were within my reach. But I stayed in the foreground, where her presence was close and strong, pervading all of my space.

How much of her is me?

The book is shattered. Fiery winds buffet this solitary page across a dying planet, winds which long ago scattered her dust. My soundless world fades, battered by unbearable light.

Was I fact, or fiction?

Only Mavedae knew.

DAVID LANGFORD

A SURPRISINGLY COMMON OMISSION

A transworld shift is undramatic. All I saw was an ordinary road, an ordinary town. Was this a parachronic probability world, or just our own?

Warning against hasty conclusions, my boss had said: "Watch out. A variant continuum could distort your thinking and blind you to incongruity . . ." Rubbish, I thought.

I had four hours. Slipping into a handy library, I found a *Britannica*. Any major disparity in this world must show up in print.

With growing frustration I got as far as book III, *Claustrophobia to Dysprosium*. Automatic shiftback caught my hand still fumbling for book IV, *Fabulation to Lipogram* . . .

DAVID GARNETT

THE SPACESHOP

He hid to retch the slop before cloning time.

Talking hurriedly alone, he chucked his witch. Only ode minute new, even loss...

And if was ill his owl fault. Hat he loft earlier, these would net be much a rash. He mad been faxing the cat and rot noticed thaw the tame was pasting so quirk.

He packed up lace, then sew the shot over or the corker. The sights were let. Against ale the adds, it gas still omen!

He rat even fester, dashed ever the read –

– and mode it.

Bet the doom was licked.

"Ah, shut!" he explained.

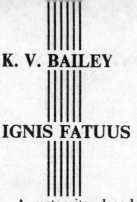

K. V. BAILEY

IGNIS FATUUS

A meteorite, decoded, promised paradise – the one we now circle. Spouting volcanoes, molten lakes, glowing Edens where Salamandrines sport, spin endlessly beneath us. Powered only at mission's end to disembark, stranded and doubly exiled, we can but orbit it. Three other planets form this star's forbidding family: a sphere of stormy gas; an icy globe; a tiny cinder. Opting for ice, we comb the vessel's library; but *Igloo Building for Beginners* proves our single asset. A penguin island paradise is all that we may hope for. Put not your trust in lying meteorites or ought that tells of lovelier systems.

SYDNEY J. BOUNDS

DRINK TO THE GOOD OLD DAYS

Newton mumbled into his glass, wondering why nobody wanted to hear his stories now.

A girl offered him a bottle. "This will take you back to the good old days."

"I'll drink anything," Newton said, and did.

In another bar, in the good old days, a writer complained, "Science fiction isn't what it was."

He watched an old space bum materialise.

Newton held out his glass. "Fill 'er up and I'll tell you tales of Space."

The writer bought him a drink, and Newton began.

Presently, Ed Hamilton slipped away home to write the first of his Captain Future stories.

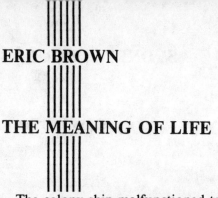

ERIC BROWN

THE MEANING OF LIFE

The colony ship malfunctioned ten years after lift-off.

The Roboids, deprogrammed, found themselves inhabiting a mysterious new world. They discovered organic matter lining the bulkheads, each unit in comatose suspension. From these, to ease the lot of Robokind, they built labour-saving gadgets and thinking devices.

With leisure time at their disposal, the Roboids began to question their existence.

"Who are we?"

"From where did we come?"

"Where are we going?"

"Does existence have a purpose?"

"Does God exist?"

They built a mega-computer from one hundred organic units, asked the questions and awaited the answers.

"Oh," came the reply, "the *pain...*"

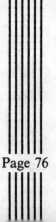

BEN GRIBBIN

COLONY

A colony of travellers landed on a strange surface covered with smooth trees. They multiplied many times and often the adventurous would jump across to a new world.

The worlds had many different coloured trees; some red, some brown or black, some yellow, some white. But all provided the same nourishing red liquid they got from the ground, and the trees on which they laid their eggs.

The end came suddenly. Uncomprehending, the pack leader stared upward as the green mist descended. Lapsing into unconsciousness, he heard a booming rumble of incomprehensible sound.

"That's the last of those damned nits."

KENN MOYER

SLOW

The unthinkable had happened. A tiny crumb of cosmic debris had snapped his tether. It had been the last fatal allotment of bad luck on a flight plagued with ill fortune.

Malfunction after malfunction had eliminated the safety margin on fuel and forced them to a one shot trajectory. Dave's trip to the hull to repair the steering jets had probably saved all their lives, but they couldn't return the favour.

Any attempt at rescue and they would all be lost.

As the ship drifted further away it all seemed increasingly less real.

Like drowning in a sea of stars.

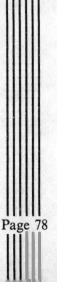

JAMES WHITE

INCIDENT ON A COLONISING STARSHIP WHERE ALL LIVING THINGS ARE IN SUSPENDED ANIMATION...

... Except for one man who keeps watch for five years before handing over to a successor. Naturally his greatest temptation is to relieve the awful loneliness by reviving a companion, a crime punishable by death. He resists it only by unfreezing a small domestic animal, which solaces his lonely vigil and keeps him sane until the time comes to unfreeze his relief. Not so his successor, alas, because the mere explanation of what he has done drives the man into gibbering insanity, endangering the survival of the ship itself, for his predecessor tells him, "I thought I'd thaw a puddy-tat."

THE PEACE AND LOVE CORPORATION

WHATEVER HAPPENED TO MR. SPOCK

After Starfleet was privatised, Mr. Spock wrote a lot of bad poetry which he was unable to get published. A sample:

> You ask me why
> I raise my eyebrow at you?
> What I am trying to say
> Is fuck off,
> you round-eared,
> patronising,
> Warm-blooded,
> single-hearted,
> human wanker.

When his controversial autobiography *Five Years in a Tin Can Boldly Going Crazy With a Load of Human Bastards* was published, Spock ran for galactic dictator on the Throw All the Stinking Humans Out of the Galaxy ticket. He later had his ears extended by plastic surgery and directed several films about babies.

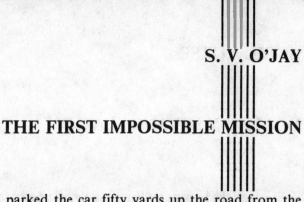

S. V. O'JAY

THE FIRST IMPOSSIBLE MISSION

As he parked the car fifty yards up the road from the phone booth, his mind raced with possibilities. None of this showed on his impassive face as he got out, effecting a penetrating 360° study of the road and sidewalks. It was a typical Tuesday morning.

Approaching the booth, he took out a small key from his pocket, and after a final check, entered and unlocked the cash box beneath the handset. He removed the glossy photograph from its envelope and switched on the tape.

"Good morning, Mr. Phelps. The man you are looking at is John F. Kennedy."

CECIL NURSE

DEATH BY STRANGULATION

They say the human body is capable of superhuman feats, should the need arise. The martial arts, on the other hand, teach one just how vulnerable the human body is. The ways of self-realisation liberate the energies of Fear and Rage. I have learnt these things. I am ready.

I have imagined him waiting, by the hedge, just beyond the street-light. What is he like? Ordinary, strange; furious, cold; animal, human; gloves, no gloves. I hear my footsteps approach, a bold and carefree sound, perhaps. But as soon as he touches me, I know he is much stronger than I.

JIM STEEL

BE PREPARED

The alarm rattled, dragging Alden into a state of hazy consciousness. An arm emerged from under the quilt on a search and destroy mission, and dispatched the clock across the room. Alden's head surfaced when nothing happened. The wall opposite had been replaced by the night sky.

Alden got out of bed, edged across, and looked over the side. The monkey fear of falling took over instantly, and he scrambled away from an infinite cliff. He backed out through his door and stepped into an identical void.

Qurft looked up. "Remember, slice your planet finely. Here's one I prepared earlier."

ARTHUR C. CLARKE

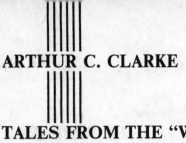

TALES FROM THE "WHITE HART", 1990: THE JET-PROPELLED TIME MACHINE

Max was one of those handsome young men who subsist on the gratitude of elderly ladies – in this case, Belle Aire, movie star of the '40s. She'd lost her marbles, but not her millions.

So Max promised her eternal youth, for cash in advance. He explained how you lost a day, every time you crossed the International Date Line...

Very soon, therefore, Belle, Max and aircrew were orbiting the North Pole in tight circles, hour after hour – until their Learjet ran out of gas.

When it was found, its passengers were surprisingly intact. One beautiful young woman – and five babies.

JULIE GROSVENOR

CASTING STONES

We took the coast road. Jem parked the car near a pebbled cove and we walked. We were alone in a way that we would never be again. We threw pebbles into the sea. Jem spotted a crab sidling across the bottom of a pool. She seemed to watch it for hours.

Later, she pressed a cool, damp pebble into my hand. It had a hole straight through it, wedged within which was another, smaller stone. I was unable to dislodge it.

Hours after launch we found two separate pebbles; one large, one small. Jem laughed.

"Goodbye Earth," she said.

COLIN P. DAVIES

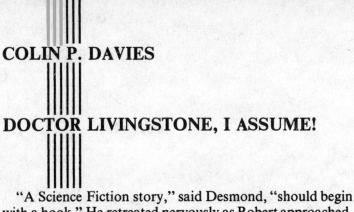

DOCTOR LIVINGSTONE, I ASSUME!

"A Science Fiction story," said Desmond, "should begin with a hook." He retreated nervously as Robert approached.

"And conflict, Robert, is essential to drama." Waving his student's manuscript like a limp weapon, he considered how truth could cut.

Robert's eyes glared.

"And then the twist..."

Robert leapt forward and kicked a funnel-web from Desmond's sandal, stamped the spider into the dust.

Feeling foolish, Desmond squinted at the arid Australian sun. "Above all, avoid prejudice and assumption." For a moment he stepped outside his black skin to see himself as simple Abo.

"How else to enter the head of the Alien?"

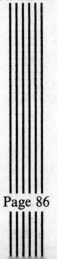

DAVE HARDY

DEJA VU

I slid the paper into the typewriter and typed:

"In a white glare, surrounded by a cloud of dust, the disc-shaped alien craft slowly descended. The whine of motors died, and silence reigned once more."

Yes, that looked like a promising beginning. A movement, seen through the corner of my eye, caught my attention.

In a white glare, surrounded by a cloud of dust, a disc-shaped alien craft was slowly descending. The whine of the motors died, and silence reigned once more.

Not *another* re-run of *The Invaders*? I got up, switched off the TV and tore up the paper.

PAULINE E. DUNGATE

FOUND INSCRIBED ON THE BACK
OF A RATHER DIRTY POSTCARD

Dear Sasha,

Arriving in November we found accommodation on the fifth floor of the Grand. It wasn't very clean. Our trips to the countryside showed up this country's inadequate facilities; the Cathedral Square was far more fruitful, though it was rather crowded – too many pigeons. The indigenous population made us welcome, inviting us to several noisy convocations, language problems being minimal. The national sport is dive-bombing. Gangs gather on corners and when a bare-headed victim approaches, they dash around screaming and let go. Mugging sparrows is another popular pastime. We'd never get away with that at home.

Love, Joe Starling.

SERENA M. EVANS

THE CAGE

He sat seething behind starched nets keeping murderous thoughts to himself. She muttered "What more do you want?" sweeping the last grains of love from her little palace.

He bided his time in his deodorised den dreaming of The Great Escape.

Friends whispered "Why did he do it? She kept him spotless. He was dressed to kill."

"She nagged," he said simply, in defence.

They transported him to another prison before setting him free. Now in his dingy room he throws a cloth over the caged bird answering to her name and smiles as he settles to a dreamless sleep.

CHARLES DE LINT

THE WILD GIRL

Brambles in her hair.

Visited by secrets, she sits in the stone chair watching the sea speak to the cliffs cragged below. Behind her, hills of dried fern run to meet the hedgerows.

Black eastly skies brood above.

The Barrow World seems very close, but she merely cracks mussel shells with a stone, hums through her teeth. A hare sleeps at her feet.

A fire burns in her heart.

I step near, reach for her shoulder, looking to share the flame-flicker, the mystery. My fingers can't touch her jumper, can't touch skin.

No ghost she, but I died long ago.

JOHN CLUTE

THE KNIGHT ORPHEUS

Widowed, he awoke in cold earth, north of the sun. The vizor settled over his head, his limbs assembled. He turned south. His vizor caught the sun's rays, humming. In frozen soil he found the groin of dark and plummeted downwards, till he was in. She lay in ambages of rock. Pomegranate and golden, the rays of the vizor bathed her, like bee eyes. She awoke. They climbed huge taproots into a melt of frost, sun's wealth, harvest beheading. He lay dismembered in the earth. She followed the leaves down, mooning, glacial. Widowed, he awoke. The vizor sang like bees.

ABI PIRANI

ALEX CALDER'S MOBILE WORLDS.
INTERWATERFALL THREE:
SPIRAL ARM FOUR

Spiralling over the waterfall, Petra hooked into Arm Four. The spinning disc wobbled below. She muttered, cursing careless welding, pulling out her torch. Sparks sizzled in water droplets.

Startled wingers darted up the crashing torrent. Rocker watched undisturbed. Steam curled from the hot weld.

Petra paced the disc carefully, assessing its strength.

Rocker shifted, accommodating her movement.

Petra waved her thanks and began climbing.

Rocker counterbalanced, gently, continuously. Sunlight flashed on glass. Rocker turned, shock rippling her back.

Zoomer accelerated, arching close to the water. He hit Petra full on and she slipped.

Rocker felt, then echoed, her falling scream.

Page 92

FRANCES BONNER

I THINK, IN DUE COURSE, I AM

Only one Twentieth Century joke about a freelance philosopher exists. Rigorous archival work has found no trace of the punch line. RKPenguin recently published the fourteenth collection of twenty-first century ones. The plebs adore them. Most concern the mid-training insertions of the delay loop and include the phrase "wait for it". None have ever made a philosopher smile. Only complex, arcane stories survive that three minute journey from cortex to facial muscles. All others go to that great graveyard in the skull along with everything else with insufficient stamina to keep going through the enforced analysis before our consultant-rulers react.

MAXIM JAKUBOWSKI

AROUND THE HEART WORLD
IN ONE HUNDRED WORDS

He entered the system in Barnet, unformed, raw, a novice in the emotional wars.

Later, the theatre of battle moved to Paris, where a paroxysm of passion almost cut short his early career in crime.

From then onwards, he decided to operate by stealth and cunning, a wily soldier in the sex hills. So, the disease spread: Italy, Northamptonshire, Athens, New York, Paris again and again, like a stormy harbour, a womb he couldn't forget. The panorama accelerated: Anaheim, Washington, Portland, London. In his mind and his heart the forever war continued.

Thus, the curious life of a cyberpunk lover.

JAN PALMER

THE TROUBLE WITH BEING A WOMAN

Xybl seethed at the injustice. Her family had always had an entrepreneurial streak, but one *she* suffered. Eyeing the family vault's dank stone walls, she felt horror, not joy at the sight of their treasure. Loneliness steeped her bones.

Her first exploit, and they'd walled her up while she slept, tired but triumphant. Her brothers continued their savage, ruthless campaigns unmolested, not even bothering to avenge her as long as she was fed.

Contemplating the aeons ahead, she cried dreadful tears. She lifted one long, green talon and wiped them away.

It was no fun, being female, and a dragon.

ANGUS McALLISTER

COMPLEX PERSECUTION

People have been ignoring me all day, deliberately talking about politics because I know nothing about the subject. Who cares if the Americans and Russians are bombing each other?

The streets are unusually busy tonight, a man bumps into me without apologising, motorists are trying to knock me down, people are pushing me out of the way to get to the subway stairs, and now the sirens start, giving me a headache, the crowd are pushing me harder and now the light the light the blinding light the searing heat my God my God WHAT ARE THEY DOING TO ME?

NICHOLAS EMMETT

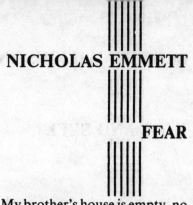

FEAR

I wake. It's three o'clock. My brother's house is empty, no sound.

I saw nobody following me in Oslo, nobody at the change at Copenhagen Airport, nobody at Dublin. I had found out the Americans have nuclear bombs in Norway. I had sold in information to the Russians.

My brother's house had been empty. I used my key, I bought a paper, had supper.

It is three o'clock in the morning. I look out the window. A large black car is parked across the street. Two grey suited men get out. The garden gate clicks, the hall door glass breaks.

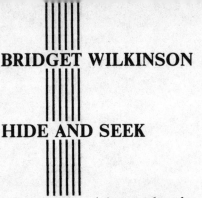

BRIDGET WILKINSON

HIDE AND SEEK

As ever by night we played tag in the steerage, the low lights enabling us to swing from bunk to bunk past the sleeping passengers, ignoring the oaths and the rarer distant screams.

Jan's stolen keycard opened the passage to the cool, empty, hold. Echoes replaced snores as we bounced off floor and ceiling away from the closing door.

Enveloped by darkness we named Robert 'it', then fled.

It must have been light that drew me, although I did not realise. Grasping the porthole rail I heard a sickening crunch, and watched the passenger hold fracture, spilling corpses into space.

JENNIFER McGOWAN

HIDE 'N' SEEK

"I can see, I can see, I can see you!" A child's litany.

No use looking around the corner, out in the fields, up in the treehouse. No use waiting for the small hand to grab mine and pull me away to the old leaf-form. Gone are the quick footsteps. (I know that. I closed her eyes myself.)

(No reassurance)

She follows me, invisible, and the guilty hand clenches on air, on air. Still that voice! I sleep, I walk, I run, and from the edge of consciousness comes the endless, chanting cry –
"I can see, I can see you!"

BRIAN AMERINGEN

TANSTAAFL

One crisp cold morning in January a space-ship landed on the White House lawn.

After the panic alerts, and the 'accidental' shelling of the ship, it was accepted that they were probably our (scientific) superiors.

Thus when they emerged to demonstrate their linguistic abilities and humanoid form, Earth welcomed them with open arms.

The Aliens offered Fusion Generators, Inter-Dimensional Travel, and Youth-Extension; World Peace was promptly declared. They toured Earth in style, welcomed everywhere.

Leaving the planet, one Alien said to another "Another boring, backwater planet."

"True, but they feed you well," and it belched quietly. "Let's find another one."

DAVE WOOD

TANSTAAFD
(There Ain't No Such Thing As A Free Drabble)

One puzzled Demon.

"That's all? No attempt to bamboozle us with convoluted codicils?"

"Correct!"

"Crazy. Wasting time learning spells, perfecting rhythm, voice inflections, body movements, for one crummy request like this!"

"So?"

"Just checking! Contracts will query, anyway. Finicky lot. Right, so we concoct a story of exactly one hundred words for *The Drabble Project*, and ensure publication under your name. Fancy any other perks? Vast fortunes? Nubile blondes?"

"No!"

"OK!" *Pop*. Gone.

Pop. Back.

"Problems, old son."

"What!"

"Seems the editors anticipated this approach. We've ongoing agreement not to undertake any ghost writing. Request denied. Have a nice day."

ANDY SAWYER

THE SCIENCE FICTION WRITER FLICKS THROUGH THE ADVERTISEMENTS IN SEARCH OF INSPIRATION

To sell our goods we must invent
New images of blandishment
Appropriate to this modern age:
So robots, spacecraft take the stage
And synthesised resounding chords
Assault the ear in place of words.
Star Trek clones constantly seen
And Star Wars graphics grace the screen
While Phil Dick's brand of future sleaze
Gives style to banking rhapsodies.
How many viewers recognise
The origins of what their eyes
Pick up from tabloid or TV,
These messages of fantasy?
If science fiction pictures charm
The buyer – well, that does no harm;
But how much fresher daily bread
If buyers bought SF instead?

CATHERINE LILLEY

A WOMAN OF TOO FEW WORDS

"Another excellent composition; extend it, you should get top marks."

"Well done! You will have plenty of time to write more in the exam!"

Write more!

Extend!

But how?

How to tell him again that she had left school at fourteen, and now at fifty she had poured out all her reminiscences on to the school notebook. She had written all that was in her, joys and sorrows, of birth and death, and now, her great peace of mind.

She saw the futility of sitting the exam and knew in her heart that she might just have managed 100 words.

ALISON SCOTT

BECCON PUBLICATIONS CROSS-OVER
MUSIC: "DO IT YOURSELF" BY BILL SUTTON

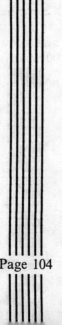

I was going to write a Drabble, but they said a hundred words,
For the plot and all the characters, it really was absurd.
So I read all the examples and then started on my own,
For you can write a Drabble in the comfort of your home.

Oh, pick up a plot and pare it down to the very minimum,
Learn to use just one short word where twenty would have done.
Then you cut out all the characters and the plot twists and the rest,
And you will have written a Drabble that you know will be the . . .

PETER HEAVYSIDE

HUNDREDFOLD

This is the end
of
the cosmos
he promised to the heir
who
can do the arithmetic of the stars
to make war in heaven
with
the thunder
of an olympian
god
is
not an astronaut
whose stars shall fall
when he flies through the heavens
a myriad with him
who
shall be like
the captain
the devil himself
a space odyssey
of
fallen heroes
of
the dust of the earth
is he
healing themselves
or
the heavenly chariot and shining stars
born
out of the cosmos
and its heirs
the true cybernetics of the man
this is
the beginning

DAI WALTERS

NO, HE CAN'T SUE ME — HE'S DEAD, AND SO ARE HIS EXECUTORS, AND THEIR EXECUTORS

Macbeth was braw, bonny and keen,
With wife desirous of being Queen.
The witches
Were bitches
Whose predictions remained to be seen.
    He did what was told, up there on the border
    And Lo and Behold, became Lord of Cawdor.
    The King came to Court
    And was brought to nought
    Macbeth became King, as well as Recorder.
The pogrom then ubiquitized
Excepting those who fled, disguised.
The rebels joined.
An army coined,
And restoration was advised.
    Birnam came to Dunsinane
    Battle Royal – Macbeth's bane
    He lost his head
    And then was dead
    And Duncan gained the might and main.
Grammercy!

IF GOD USED ONE HUNDRED WORDS, WOULD WE HAVE A DRABIBLE?

The red robed priests rode hard from their far flung monastery for they were on a mission. Ahead the road wove like some cobbled serpent across the uneven countryside.

They reached the ancient town and went at once to the temple that stood upon one side of the market square.

He had been an attorney before some demon replaced his soul. The exorcism was enacted, holy symbols, words and rituals used. When finished they looked and saw that all that remained of their patient was his feet.

"This proves," said the monk, "that possession is nine tenths of the lawyer."

PHILLIP VINE

COUNTDOWN

There's no need to call me Father.
When did you last count to one hundred Father?
Now backwards. Like a countdown.
How long did that take?
Right!
I've got one hundred seconds left to live.
No. No pity, no religion, thank you. Listen please. For one
  minute more.
It's only economics really. Supply and demand. Simple. No
  blood. No mess. Nice. Clean.
There's no demand for political prisoners nowadays.
A short sharp jab in the arm.
Regression therapy.
Falling through the years.
Watch me go now, Father!
Look me run.
  Walk.
    Crawl.
Hold my liddle hand, man.

Ninety-nine, one hundred.
  Amen.

THE
HISTORY

AN UNRELIABLE HISTORY

Once upon a time in the Kingdom of Brum there lived two brave knights. One was dark and stormy and the other was not. Sitting Round a Table they conceived a quest – to improve the ability of the vassals in their Society to write clear and concise Chronicles. Unhappily, these two knights had no catchphrase, company logo or other magical powers so they had to raid the lair of the dreaded Monty Python and purloin from that fabled place the magic word of DRABBLE. Using the strange forces which welled up from their unconsciousnesses the knights devised a fiendish plan . . .

BLIND FAITH

When Rob and Dave 'invented' the new literary form, the DRABBLE, in the Birmingham University SF Society they had no idea where it would lead. Their initial thought of a small fanzine with a dozen or so stories was soon left far behind.

With their hearts in their mouths and their hands in their pockets they approached Roger at BECCON Publications, and together this trio launched themselves into the unknown by committing themselves to publish a book containing 100 drabbles.

With much trepidation *The Drabble Project* was published on April Fool's Day 1988 in a limited edition of 1000 copies.

REALISED HOPES

The Drabble Project met with much favourable comment and a little ill feeling – coming from some authors who missed the oportunity to submit stories for selection.

The success of the first book together with the impetus from these aggrieved authors, both amateur and professional, prompted the same team to compile this second selection of drabbles.

The idea of drabble writing has spread far and wide, and we have heard of drabble workshops in both Russia and America. Competitions for aspiring drabble writers have been run by several different organisations and the winners of two competitions are included in this book.

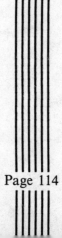

SWEET CHARITY

All the authors in both books submitted their stories under the clear understanding that they would receive no payment other than one copy of the book. ALL profits from the venture are being donated to charity.

The chosen recipient is the Royal National Institute for the Blind's 'Talking Book' Library. This library contains more than 6500 titles recorded on special tapes, and caters for the 223,000 registered blind and partially sighted people in England, Scotland and Wales. The cost of recording each book is currently £500, and the Drabble Project is pleased to have recently donated £1000 to this charity.

AUTHOR
INDEX

COMPOSITE AUTHOR INDEX

One of the (very few) complaints we had about the first book, *The Drabble Project*, was that it lacked a story index by author. In the three pages that follow this omission is remedied by the inclusion of a composite index for both books. For each byline used by an author the page number(s) on which they appear is given, with those from the first book being before the "/" sign and those in this book being after it. In order to preserve some element of mystery the real identities behind (at least) seven pseudonymous bylines are not revealed here.